Mice Mischief

An Alphabet Story

Written by Susan Blackaby

Illustrated by Joe Boddy

McGraw-Hill School Division

New York   Farmington

Dee and Bink want to see the palace.
So they climb the **apple** tree.

"Look at the **bed**," said Dee.

"Look at that **cat**!" said Bink.

"Run to the **desk**!" said Dee.

Bink gets stuck on the **edge**.

Dee and Bink hide by the **fan**.
"We must **get** out of here!" said Bink.

Dee gets in the **hat**.
Bink cannot get **in**.

Bink hides behind the **jar**.

The mice run past the **king**.

They run up a **ladder**.

They see a **man**.

The man has a **net**!

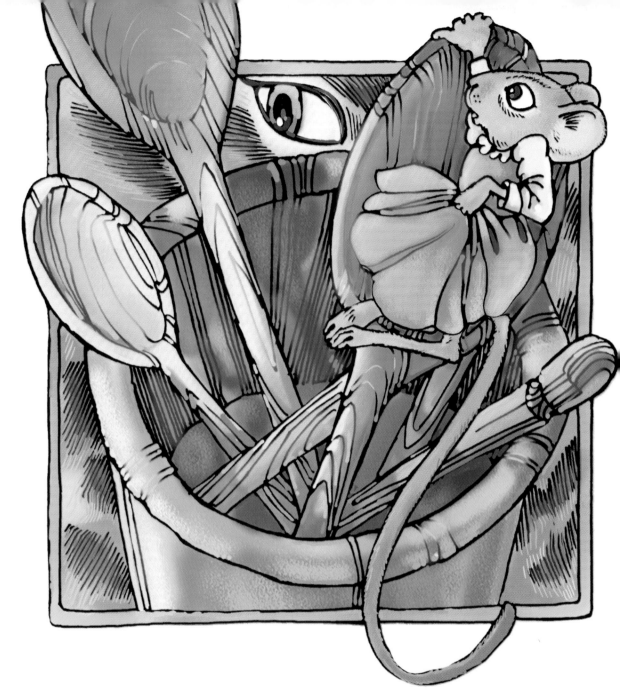

Dee hangs **on** a spoon.

Bink hides in a **pot**.

They tiptoe **quietly** past the dog.

They run under the **rug**.

Dee hides by the **salt**.

Bink runs across the **table**.

Bink hides **under** a napkin.

Then Bink tears his **vest**!

"Let's try the **window**!" said Dee.

"I found an **exit**!" said Dee.

The mice run across the **yard**.

And they **zig-zag**
all the way home!